HELP!

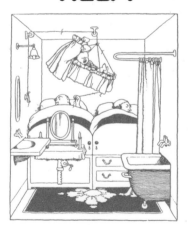

HELP!

A Record Book for Household Names, Notes & Numbers

With illustrations by W. Heath Robinson

THE METROPOLITAN MUSEUM OF ART • NEW YORK
A BULFINCH PRESS BOOK
LITTLE, BROWN AND COMPANY
BOSTON • NEW YORK • TORONTO • LONDON

Second edition, 1996

ISBN 0-87099-763-7 (MMA)
ISBN 0-8212-2365-8 (Bulfinch)

Published by The Metropolitan Museum of Art and Bulfinch Press
Bulfinch is an imprint and trademark of
Little, Brown and Company (Inc.)
Published simultaneously in Canada by
Little, Brown & Company (Canada) Limited

Produced by the Department of Special Publications,
The Metropolitan Museum of Art
Design by Marleen Adlerblum
Cover design by Tina Fjotland

PRINTED IN HONG KONG

ABOUT W. HEATH ROBINSON

Born in London into a family of professional artists, W. Heath Robinson (1872–1944) initially achieved success as a book illustrator, capable of a diversity of styles and effects. A contemporary of Edmund Dulac and Arthur Rackham, Heath Robinson illustrated more than sixty books, including *Don Quixote*, *The Arabian Nights*, poems by Edgar Allan Poe, and color-plate editions of *A Midsummer Night's Dream* and Hans Christian Andersen's *Fairy Tales*.

While making a name for himself as a book illustrator, Heath Robinson also achieved notoriety as a comic illustrator. During the 1930s he was dubbed "the gadget king," his name synonymous with fantastic machinery, elaborate gadgets, and ludicrous contraptions. A diversity of inventions, from a six-tier communal cradle for babysitters to a magnetic figure preserver for the middle-aged, emerged from his fertile imagination. As he was later to note in his autobiography, *My Line of Life*, "My name became so closely associated with humorous work, and a by-word for a certain kind of absurdity, that my signature on more serious drawings was, I admit, disconcerting."

It was not enough for Heath Robinson that his ideas were funny; the way they were expressed had to be equally humorous—a task that the artist took very seriously. "There must always be this co-operation between the jester and his audience," he explained. "It takes two at least to make a successful joke." Displaying quality draftsmanship and keen observation, Heath Robinson's drawings are rooted in the great tradition of British comic art. Heath Robinson himself attributed much of the success of his comic illustrations to their linear style, an inimitable technique in which no detail was omitted.

Despite his meticulous rendering of contraptions and gadgets, Heath Robinson pleaded complete ignorance of machinery of any kind. His inventions, however, are convincing enough to make his absurdly fantastic view of life plausible. It is difficult to resist laughter at his elaborate solutions to everyday problems and the innocent characters who populate his comic world.

The illustrations in *Help!* are taken from a series of "How to" books illustrated by W. Heath Robinson in the 1930s. Those books, in the collection of the Department of Drawings and Prints of The Metropolitan Museum of Art, include *How to Be a Motorist*, *How to Be a Perfect Husband*, *How to Build a New World*, *How to Live in a Flat*, *How to Make Your Garden Grow*, *How to Run a Communal Home*, and *Let's Laugh*. They were first published in London by Hutchinson & Co. between 1936 and 1943.

CONTENTS

EMERGENCY INFORMATION 8
PERSONAL INFORMATION 9

ACCOUNTANTS 10
AIRLINES 11
ANTIQUE & ART DEALERS 13
ARCHITECTS 16
AUDIO/VIDEO EQUIPMENT 17
AUTOMOBILE RENTAL 19
AUTOMOTIVE SERVICES 21
BABYSITTERS 24
BAKERIES 28
BANKS 29
BARTENDERS 30
BATHROOM FIXTURES 31
BEAUTICIANS 32
BOOKSHOPS 33
BUILDERS 34
BUS LINES 36
BUTCHERS 37
CABINETMAKERS 38
CARPENTERS 40
CARPET CLEANERS 42
CAR POOLS 43
CATERERS 44
CHILD CARE 46
CHURCHES 51
CLEANING SERVICES 52
CLOCKS & WATCHES 54
CLOTHING STORES 56
COMPUTERS 59
CONTRACTORS 60
COUNTRY CLUBS 61
CRAFT STORES 63
DENTISTS 64
DEPARTMENT STORES 66

DOCTORS 67
DRY CLEANERS 70
ELECTRICIANS 72
ESTIMATORS 74
EXTERMINATORS 75
FABRIC STORES 77
FIREPLACES 79
FIREWOOD 80
FLOORS & FLOOR
   COVERINGS 81
FLORISTS 84
FURNITURE 86
GARAGES 90
GARBAGE REMOVAL 92
GLASSWARE & CHINA 93
GOURMET SHOPS 94
GROCERY STORES 95
HAIRDRESSERS & BARBERS ... 96
HANDYMAN 97
HARDWARE STORES 98
HEALTH CLUBS 100
HEATING & COOLING
   SYSTEMS 102
HOSPITALS 104
HOTELS 105
HOUSE SITTERS 108
INSURANCE AGENCIES 109
INTERIOR DECORATORS 110
INVESTMENT ADVISORS 112
JEWELERS 113
KENNELS 114
KITCHEN APPLIANCES &
   EQUIPMENT 115
LANDSCAPERS 118
LAUNDRY SERVICES 119
LAWN CARE 120
LAWYERS 122

CONTENTS

LIBRARIES 123

LIGHTING 124

LINENS 126

LIQUOR STORES 128

LOCKSMITHS 129

LUMBERYARDS 130

MAILING SERVICES 131

MARINAS 132

MESSENGER SERVICES 133

MOVERS 134

MUSICAL INSTRUMENTS 135

NEWSPAPERS 136

NURSES 137

PAINTERS 138

PARTY RENTALS 140

PET GROOMING 142

PHARMACIES 144

PHOTOGRAPHIC SERVICES . . . 145

PIANO TUNERS 146

PICTURE FRAMERS 147

PLANT NURSERIES 148

PLUMBERS 150

POST OFFICES 152

RAILROADS 154

REAL-ESTATE AGENCIES 155

RECORD STORES 157

RESTAURANTS 158

ROOFING 163

SCHOOLS 164

SECURITY SYSTEMS 167

SHOE REPAIR 168

SHOE STORES 169

SOUND PROOFING 170

SPORTING GOODS 172

STORAGE SERVICES 174

SWIMMING POOLS 176

SYNAGOGUES 177

TAILORS & DRESSMAKERS 178

TAKE-OUT RESTAURANTS 180

TAXIS & LIMOUSINES 183

TELEPHONES 184

TELEVISION & RADIO 186

TENNIS COURTS 187

**THEATERS & PERFORMANCE
    HALLS** 189

TRAVEL AGENCIES 191

TREE SERVICES 192

TYPING SERVICES 193

UPHOLSTERERS 194

VETERINARIANS 196

WALLPAPER 198

WATERPROOFING 200

WINDOWS 202

HELP! HELP! HELP! 206

EMERGENCY INFORMATION

AMBULANCE_____

FIRE_____

POLICE_____

DOCTOR_____

  OFFICE TELEPHONE_____HOME TELEPHONE_____

OTHER EMERGENCY NUMBERS

_____

_____

_____

_____

_____

_____

IN CASE OF ACCIDENT OR ILLNESS NOTIFY:

NAME_____

ADDRESS_____

OFFICE TELEPHONE_____

HOME TELEPHONE_____

FAMILY MEDICAL INFORMATION

NAME_____

  BLOOD GROUP_____ALLERGIES_____MEDIC ALERT_____

NAME_____

  BLOOD GROUP_____ALLERGIES_____MEDIC ALERT_____

NAME_____

  BLOOD GROUP_____ALLERGIES_____MEDIC ALERT_____

NAME_____

  BLOOD GROUP_____ALLERGIES_____MEDIC ALERT_____

FINANCIAL

	INSTITUTION	ACCOUNT OR POLICY NUMBER
CHECKING ACCOUNT(S)		
SAVINGS ACCOUNT(S)		
INSURANCE: AUTO, HEALTH, HOME, LIFE		
OTHER ASSETS		

CREDIT CARDS

NAME	NUMBER	EXPIRATION DATE

AUTOMOBILE

MAKE OF AUTO(S) _____

REGISTRATION NUMBER(S) _____

LICENSE PLATE NUMBER(S) _____

DRIVER'S LICENSE NUMBER(S) _____

EXPIRATION DATE(S) _____

ACCOUNTANTS

NAME

ADDRESS

PHONE

REFERRED BY

COMMENTS

NAME

ADDRESS

PHONE

REFERRED BY

COMMENTS

NAME

ADDRESS

PHONE

REFERRED BY

COMMENTS

NAME

ADDRESS

PHONE

REFERRED BY

COMMENTS

NAME _____

ADDRESS _____

PHONE _____

REFERRED BY _____

COMMENTS _____

_____

NAME _____

ADDRESS _____

PHONE _____

REFERRED BY _____

COMMENTS _____

_____

The air honeymoon

AIRLINES

NAME

ADDRESS

PHONE

REFERRED BY

COMMENTS

NAME

ADDRESS

PHONE

REFERRED BY

COMMENTS

NAME

ADDRESS

PHONE

REFERRED BY

COMMENTS

NAME

ADDRESS

PHONE

REFERRED BY

COMMENTS

NAME

ADDRESS

PHONE

REFERRED BY

COMMENTS

NAME

ADDRESS

PHONE

REFERRED BY

COMMENTS

NAME

ADDRESS

PHONE

REFERRED BY

COMMENTS

NAME

ADDRESS

PHONE

REFERRED BY

COMMENTS

Converted wedding presents

NAME

ADDRESS

PHONE

REFERRED BY

COMMENTS

NAME

ADDRESS

PHONE

REFERRED BY

COMMENTS

NAME

ADDRESS

PHONE

REFERRED BY

COMMENTS

NAME

ADDRESS

PHONE

REFERRED BY

COMMENTS

ARCHITECTS

NAME

ADDRESS

PHONE

REFERRED BY

COMMENTS

NAME

ADDRESS

PHONE

REFERRED BY

COMMENTS

NAME

ADDRESS

PHONE

REFERRED BY

COMMENTS

NAME

ADDRESS

PHONE

REFERRED BY

COMMENTS

NAME

ADDRESS

PHONE

REFERRED BY

COMMENTS

NAME

ADDRESS

PHONE

REFERRED BY

COMMENTS

NAME

ADDRESS

PHONE

REFERRED BY

COMMENTS

NAME

ADDRESS

PHONE

REFERRED BY

COMMENTS

NAME

ADDRESS

PHONE

REFERRED BY

COMMENTS

NAME

ADDRESS

PHONE

REFERRED BY

COMMENTS

NAME

ADDRESS

PHONE

REFERRED BY

COMMENTS

NAME

ADDRESS

PHONE

REFERRED BY

COMMENTS

NAME _____

ADDRESS _____

PHONE _____

REFERRED BY _____

COMMENTS _____

_____

NAME _____

ADDRESS _____

PHONE _____

REFERRED BY _____

COMMENTS _____

_____

The duo-car for the incompatible

AUTOMOBILE RENTAL

NAME

ADDRESS

PHONE

REFERRED BY

COMMENTS

NAME

ADDRESS

PHONE

REFERRED BY

COMMENTS

NAME

ADDRESS

PHONE

REFERRED BY

COMMENTS

NAME

ADDRESS

PHONE

REFERRED BY

COMMENTS

NAME

ADDRESS

PHONE

REFERRED BY

COMMENTS

The "expandocar"

NAME

ADDRESS

PHONE

REFERRED BY

COMMENTS

expanded

AUTOMOTIVE SERVICES

NAME

ADDRESS

PHONE

REFERRED BY

COMMENTS

NAME

ADDRESS

PHONE

REFERRED BY

COMMENTS

The new safety street for learners

NAME

ADDRESS

PHONE

REFERRED BY

COMMENTS

NAME

ADDRESS

PHONE

REFERRED BY

COMMENTS

The extending garage for cars of all sizes

NAME _____

ADDRESS _____

PHONE _____

REFERRED BY _____

COMMENTS _____

_____

NAME _____

ADDRESS _____

PHONE _____

REFERRED BY _____

COMMENTS _____

_____

The morning walk

NAME _____

ADDRESS _____

PHONE _____

REFERRED BY _____

COMMENTS _____

_____

NAME _____

ADDRESS _____

PHONE _____

REFERRED BY _____

COMMENTS _____

_____

NAME _____

ADDRESS _____

PHONE _____

REFERRED BY _____

COMMENTS _____

_____

NAME _____

ADDRESS _____

PHONE _____

REFERRED BY _____

COMMENTS _____

_____

The six-tier communal cradle

NAME

ADDRESS

PHONE

REFERRED BY

COMMENTS

NAME

ADDRESS

PHONE

REFERRED BY

COMMENTS

NAME

ADDRESS

PHONE

REFERRED BY

COMMENTS

NAME

ADDRESS

PHONE

REFERRED BY

COMMENTS

BAKERIES

NAME

ADDRESS

PHONE

REFERRED BY

COMMENTS

NAME

ADDRESS

PHONE

REFERRED BY

COMMENTS

NAME

ADDRESS

PHONE

REFERRED BY

COMMENTS

NAME

ADDRESS

PHONE

REFERRED BY

COMMENTS

NAME

ADDRESS

PHONE

REFERRED BY

COMMENTS

NAME

ADDRESS

PHONE

REFERRED BY

COMMENTS

NAME

ADDRESS

PHONE

REFERRED BY

COMMENTS

NAME

ADDRESS

PHONE

REFERRED BY

COMMENTS

BARTENDERS

NAME

ADDRESS

PHONE

REFERRED BY

COMMENTS

NAME

ADDRESS

PHONE

REFERRED BY

COMMENTS

NAME

ADDRESS

PHONE

REFERRED BY

COMMENTS

NAME

ADDRESS

PHONE

REFERRED BY

COMMENTS

NAME _____

ADDRESS _____

PHONE _____

REFERRED BY _____

COMMENTS _____

_____

NAME _____

ADDRESS _____

PHONE _____

REFERRED BY _____

COMMENTS _____

_____

The combination bath and writing desk for business men

BEAUTICIANS

NAME

ADDRESS

PHONE

REFERRED BY

COMMENTS

NAME

ADDRESS

PHONE

REFERRED BY

COMMENTS

NAME

ADDRESS

PHONE

REFERRED BY

COMMENTS

NAME

ADDRESS

PHONE

REFERRED BY

COMMENTS

NAME _____

ADDRESS _____

PHONE _____

REFERRED BY _____

COMMENTS _____

_____

NAME _____

ADDRESS _____

PHONE _____

REFERRED BY _____

COMMENTS _____

_____

When you want a quiet read in the evening

NAME _____

ADDRESS _____

PHONE _____

REFERRED BY _____

COMMENTS _____

_____

⚒

NAME _____

ADDRESS _____

PHONE _____

REFERRED BY _____

COMMENTS _____

_____

Thin walls

NAME _____

ADDRESS _____

PHONE _____

REFERRED BY _____

COMMENTS _____

_____

NAME _____

ADDRESS _____

PHONE _____

REFERRED BY _____

COMMENTS _____

_____

NAME _____

ADDRESS _____

PHONE _____

REFERRED BY _____

COMMENTS _____

_____

NAME _____

ADDRESS _____

PHONE _____

REFERRED BY _____

COMMENTS _____

_____

BUS LINES

NAME

ADDRESS

PHONE

REFERRED BY

COMMENTS

NAME

ADDRESS

PHONE

REFERRED BY

COMMENTS

NAME

ADDRESS

PHONE

REFERRED BY

COMMENTS

NAME

ADDRESS

PHONE

REFERRED BY

COMMENTS

NAME

ADDRESS

PHONE

REFERRED BY

COMMENTS

NAME

ADDRESS

PHONE

REFERRED BY

COMMENTS

NAME

ADDRESS

PHONE

REFERRED BY

COMMENTS

NAME

ADDRESS

PHONE

REFERRED BY

COMMENTS

CABINETMAKERS

NAME

ADDRESS

PHONE

REFERRED BY

COMMENTS

NAME

ADDRESS

PHONE

REFERRED BY

COMMENTS

NAME

ADDRESS

PHONE

REFERRED BY

COMMENTS

NAME

ADDRESS

PHONE

REFERRED BY

COMMENTS

NAME

ADDRESS

PHONE

REFERRED BY

COMMENTS

NAME

ADDRESS

PHONE

REFERRED BY

COMMENTS

Modern dressing-room furniture

NAME

ADDRESS

PHONE

REFERRED BY

COMMENTS

NAME

ADDRESS

PHONE

REFERRED BY

COMMENTS

Weak hinges

NAME

ADDRESS

PHONE

REFERRED BY

COMMENTS

NAME

ADDRESS

PHONE

REFERRED BY

COMMENTS

NAME

ADDRESS

PHONE

REFERRED BY

COMMENTS

NAME

ADDRESS

PHONE

REFERRED BY

COMMENTS

CARPET CLEANERS

NAME _____

ADDRESS _____

PHONE _____

REFERRED BY _____

COMMENTS _____

_____

NAME _____

ADDRESS _____

PHONE _____

REFERRED BY _____

COMMENTS _____

_____

NAME _____

ADDRESS _____

PHONE _____

REFERRED BY _____

COMMENTS _____

_____

NAME _____

ADDRESS _____

PHONE _____

REFERRED BY _____

COMMENTS _____

_____

NAME

ADDRESS

PHONE

REFERRED BY

COMMENTS

NAME

ADDRESS

PHONE

REFERRED BY

COMMENTS

NAME

ADDRESS

PHONE

REFERRED BY

COMMENTS

NAME

ADDRESS

PHONE

REFERRED BY

COMMENTS

CATERERS

NAME

ADDRESS

PHONE

REFERRED BY

COMMENTS

NAME

ADDRESS

PHONE

REFERRED BY

COMMENTS

NAME

ADDRESS

PHONE

REFERRED BY

COMMENTS

NAME

ADDRESS

PHONE

REFERRED BY

COMMENTS

NAME _____

ADDRESS _____

PHONE _____

REFERRED BY _____

COMMENTS _____

_____

NAME _____

ADDRESS _____

PHONE _____

REFERRED BY _____

COMMENTS _____

_____

An improved dinner-wagon

CHILD CARE

NAME

ADDRESS

PHONE

REFERRED BY

COMMENTS

NAME

ADDRESS

PHONE

REFERRED BY

COMMENTS

NAME

ADDRESS

PHONE

REFERRED BY

COMMENTS

NAME

ADDRESS

PHONE

REFERRED BY

COMMENTS

NAME _____

ADDRESS _____

PHONE _____

REFERRED BY _____

COMMENTS _____

_____

Pets' playground, Tryplit Mansions

NAME

ADDRESS

PHONE

REFERRED BY

COMMENTS

A perfect husband

NAME

ADDRESS

PHONE

REFERRED BY

COMMENTS

NAME

ADDRESS

PHONE

REFERRED BY

COMMENTS

NAME

ADDRESS

PHONE

REFERRED BY

COMMENTS

NAME

ADDRESS

PHONE

REFERRED BY

COMMENTS

CHILD CARE

NAME

ADDRESS

PHONE

REFERRED BY

COMMENTS

NAME

ADDRESS

PHONE

REFERRED BY

COMMENTS

For keeping a child at her practice

NAME

ADDRESS

PHONE

REFERRED BY

COMMENTS

NAME

ADDRESS

PHONE

REFERRED BY

COMMENTS

NAME

ADDRESS

PHONE

REFERRED BY

COMMENTS

NAME

ADDRESS

PHONE

REFERRED BY

COMMENTS

CLEANING SERVICES

NAME

ADDRESS

PHONE

REFERRED BY

COMMENTS

NAME

ADDRESS

PHONE

REFERRED BY

COMMENTS

NAME

ADDRESS

PHONE

REFERRED BY

COMMENTS

NAME

ADDRESS

PHONE

REFERRED BY

COMMENTS

NAME

ADDRESS

PHONE

REFERRED BY

COMMENTS

NAME

ADDRESS

PHONE

REFERRED BY

COMMENTS

NAME

ADDRESS

PHONE

REFERRED BY

COMMENTS

The daily dust collection

NAME _____

ADDRESS _____

PHONE _____

REFERRED BY _____

COMMENTS _____

_____

NAME _____

ADDRESS _____

PHONE _____

REFERRED BY _____

COMMENTS _____

_____

To save the trouble of asking the time of a policeman

NAME _____

ADDRESS _____

PHONE _____

REFERRED BY _____

COMMENTS _____

_____

NAME _____

ADDRESS _____

PHONE _____

REFERRED BY _____

COMMENTS _____

_____

NAME _____

ADDRESS _____

PHONE _____

REFERRED BY _____

COMMENTS _____

_____

NAME _____

ADDRESS _____

PHONE _____

REFERRED BY _____

COMMENTS _____

_____

NAME

ADDRESS

PHONE

REFERRED BY

COMMENTS

Gent.'s bathing-suit for evening wear

NAME _____

ADDRESS _____

PHONE _____

REFERRED BY _____

COMMENTS _____

_____

NAME _____

ADDRESS _____

PHONE _____

REFERRED BY _____

COMMENTS _____

_____

NAME _____

ADDRESS _____

PHONE _____

REFERRED BY _____

COMMENTS _____

_____

NAME _____

ADDRESS _____

PHONE _____

REFERRED BY _____

COMMENTS _____

_____

CLOTHING STORES

NAME

ADDRESS

PHONE

REFERRED BY

COMMENTS

NAME

ADDRESS

PHONE

REFERRED BY

COMMENTS

NAME

ADDRESS

PHONE

REFERRED BY

COMMENTS

NAME

ADDRESS

PHONE

REFERRED BY

COMMENTS

NAME

ADDRESS

PHONE

REFERRED BY

COMMENTS

NAME

ADDRESS

PHONE

REFERRED BY

COMMENTS

NAME

ADDRESS

PHONE

REFERRED BY

COMMENTS

NAME

ADDRESS

PHONE

REFERRED BY

COMMENTS

CONTRACTORS

NAME _____

ADDRESS _____

PHONE _____

REFERRED BY _____

COMMENTS _____

_____

NAME _____

ADDRESS _____

PHONE _____

REFERRED BY _____

COMMENTS _____

_____

NAME _____

ADDRESS _____

PHONE _____

REFERRED BY _____

COMMENTS _____

_____

NAME _____

ADDRESS _____

PHONE _____

REFERRED BY _____

COMMENTS _____

_____

NAME _____

ADDRESS _____

PHONE _____

REFERRED BY _____

COMMENTS _____

_____

A round of golf at Dorisdene Mansions

COUNTRY CLUBS

NAME

ADDRESS

PHONE

REFERRED BY

COMMENTS

NAME

ADDRESS

PHONE

REFERRED BY

COMMENTS

NAME

ADDRESS

PHONE

REFERRED BY

COMMENTS

NAME

ADDRESS

PHONE

REFERRED BY

COMMENTS

NAME

ADDRESS

PHONE

REFERRED BY

COMMENTS

NAME

ADDRESS

PHONE

REFERRED BY

COMMENTS

NAME

ADDRESS

PHONE

REFERRED BY

COMMENTS

Helping with the jumper

DENTISTS

NAME _____

ADDRESS _____

PHONE _____

REFERRED BY _____

COMMENTS _____

_____

NAME _____

ADDRESS _____

PHONE _____

REFERRED BY _____

COMMENTS _____

_____

NAME _____

ADDRESS _____

PHONE _____

REFERRED BY _____

COMMENTS _____

_____

*Dental inspection
with no fuss*

NAME

ADDRESS

PHONE

REFERRED BY

COMMENTS

NAME

ADDRESS

PHONE

REFERRED BY

COMMENTS

NAME

ADDRESS

PHONE

REFERRED BY

COMMENTS

NAME

ADDRESS

PHONE

REFERRED BY

COMMENTS

DEPARTMENT STORES

NAME

ADDRESS

PHONE

REFERRED BY

COMMENTS

NAME

ADDRESS

PHONE

REFERRED BY

COMMENTS

NAME

ADDRESS

PHONE

REFERRED BY

COMMENTS

NAME

ADDRESS

PHONE

REFERRED BY

COMMENTS

NAME

ADDRESS

PHONE

REFERRED BY

COMMENTS

NAME

ADDRESS

PHONE

REFERRED BY

COMMENTS

NAME

ADDRESS

PHONE

REFERRED BY

COMMENTS

NAME

ADDRESS

PHONE

REFERRED BY

COMMENTS

DOCTORS

NAME

ADDRESS

PHONE

REFERRED BY

COMMENTS

NAME

ADDRESS

PHONE

REFERRED BY

COMMENTS

NAME

ADDRESS

PHONE

REFERRED BY

COMMENTS

NAME

ADDRESS

PHONE

REFERRED BY

COMMENTS

NAME

ADDRESS

PHONE

REFERRED BY

COMMENTS

*Ingenious ruse for administering a dose of medicine
to a boisterous boy*

DRY CLEANERS

NAME _____

ADDRESS _____

PHONE _____

REFERRED BY _____

COMMENTS _____

_____

NAME _____

ADDRESS _____

PHONE _____

REFERRED BY _____

COMMENTS _____

_____

NAME _____

ADDRESS _____

PHONE _____

REFERRED BY _____

COMMENTS _____

The soup tie

NAME

ADDRESS

PHONE

REFERRED BY

COMMENTS

NAME

ADDRESS

PHONE

REFERRED BY

COMMENTS

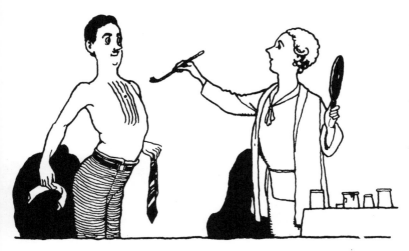

When the shirt does not come home from the wash

NAME _____

ADDRESS _____

PHONE _____

REFERRED BY _____

COMMENTS _____

_____

NAME _____

ADDRESS _____

PHONE _____

REFERRED BY _____

COMMENTS _____

_____

NAME _____

ADDRESS _____

PHONE _____

REFERRED BY _____

COMMENTS _____

_____

NAME _____

ADDRESS _____

PHONE _____

REFERRED BY _____

COMMENTS _____

_____

Replacing a fuse

NAME

ADDRESS

PHONE

REFERRED BY

COMMENTS

NAME

ADDRESS

PHONE

REFERRED BY

COMMENTS

NAME

ADDRESS

PHONE

REFERRED BY

COMMENTS

NAME

ADDRESS

PHONE

REFERRED BY

COMMENTS

NAME _____

ADDRESS _____

PHONE _____

REFERRED BY _____

COMMENTS _____

An effective wasp gun

EXTERMINATORS

NAME

ADDRESS

PHONE

REFERRED BY

COMMENTS

NAME

ADDRESS

PHONE

REFERRED BY

COMMENTS

NAME

ADDRESS

PHONE

REFERRED BY

COMMENTS

NAME

ADDRESS

PHONE

REFERRED BY

COMMENTS

NAME

ADDRESS

PHONE

REFERRED BY

COMMENTS

An awkward predicament —

NAME

ADDRESS

PHONE

REFERRED BY

COMMENTS

and an artistic way out of it

FABRIC STORES

NAME

ADDRESS

PHONE

REFERRED BY

COMMENTS

NAME

ADDRESS

PHONE

REFERRED BY

COMMENTS

NAME

ADDRESS

PHONE

REFERRED BY

COMMENTS

NAME

ADDRESS

PHONE

REFERRED BY

COMMENTS

NAME

ADDRESS

PHONE

REFERRED BY

COMMENTS

NAME

ADDRESS

PHONE

REFERRED BY

COMMENTS

When the kitchen chimney catches fire

FIREWOOD

NAME

ADDRESS

PHONE

REFERRED BY

COMMENTS

NAME

ADDRESS

PHONE

REFERRED BY

COMMENTS

NAME

ADDRESS

PHONE

REFERRED BY

COMMENTS

NAME

ADDRESS

PHONE

REFERRED BY

COMMENTS

NAME

ADDRESS

PHONE

REFERRED BY

COMMENTS

NAME

ADDRESS

PHONE

REFERRED BY

COMMENTS

NAME

ADDRESS

PHONE

REFERRED BY

COMMENTS

NAME

ADDRESS

PHONE

REFERRED BY

COMMENTS

NAME

ADDRESS

PHONE

REFERRED BY

COMMENTS

NAME

ADDRESS

PHONE

REFERRED BY

COMMENTS

NAME

ADDRESS

PHONE

REFERRED BY

COMMENTS

NAME

ADDRESS

PHONE

REFERRED BY

COMMENTS

NAME

ADDRESS

PHONE

REFERRED BY

COMMENTS

Modern carpet designs may provide endless entertainment for your friends

NAME _____

ADDRESS _____

PHONE _____

REFERRED BY _____

COMMENTS _____

_____

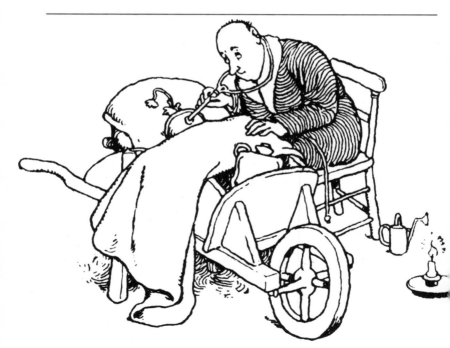

NAME _____

ADDRESS _____

PHONE _____

REFERRED BY _____

COMMENTS _____

_____

A sick chrysanthemum

NAME

ADDRESS

PHONE

REFERRED BY

COMMENTS

NAME

ADDRESS

PHONE

REFERRED BY

COMMENTS

NAME

ADDRESS

PHONE

REFERRED BY

COMMENTS

NAME

ADDRESS

PHONE

REFERRED BY

COMMENTS

NAME

ADDRESS

PHONE

REFERRED BY

COMMENTS

NAME

ADDRESS

PHONE

REFERRED BY

COMMENTS

NAME

ADDRESS

PHONE

REFERRED BY

COMMENTS

NAME

ADDRESS

PHONE

REFERRED BY

COMMENTS

NAME

ADDRESS

PHONE

REFERRED BY

COMMENTS

NAME

ADDRESS

PHONE

REFERRED BY

COMMENTS

The one-piece chromium steel dining suite

NAME

ADDRESS

PHONE

REFERRED BY

COMMENTS

NAME

ADDRESS

PHONE

REFERRED BY

COMMENTS

Chaste design in chromium

NAME

ADDRESS

PHONE

REFERRED BY

COMMENTS

NAME

ADDRESS

PHONE

REFERRED BY

COMMENTS

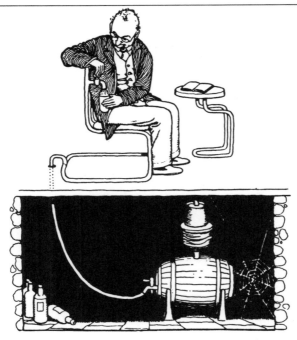

An interesting development in tubular steel furniture

NAME

ADDRESS

PHONE

REFERRED BY

COMMENTS

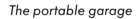

NAME

ADDRESS

PHONE

REFERRED BY

COMMENTS

The portable garage

NAME _____

ADDRESS _____

PHONE _____

REFERRED BY _____

COMMENTS _____

_____

NAME _____

ADDRESS _____

PHONE _____

REFERRED BY _____

COMMENTS _____

_____

NAME _____

ADDRESS _____

PHONE _____

REFERRED BY _____

COMMENTS _____

_____

NAME _____

ADDRESS _____

PHONE _____

REFERRED BY _____

COMMENTS _____

_____

GARBAGE REMOVAL

NAME

ADDRESS

PHONE

REFERRED BY

COMMENTS

NAME

ADDRESS

PHONE

REFERRED BY

COMMENTS

NAME

ADDRESS

PHONE

REFERRED BY

COMMENTS

NAME

ADDRESS

PHONE

REFERRED BY

COMMENTS

NAME

ADDRESS

PHONE

REFERRED BY

COMMENTS

NAME

ADDRESS

PHONE

REFERRED BY

COMMENTS

NAME

ADDRESS

PHONE

REFERRED BY

COMMENTS

NAME

ADDRESS

PHONE

REFERRED BY

COMMENTS

GOURMET SHOPS

NAME

ADDRESS

PHONE

REFERRED BY

COMMENTS

NAME

ADDRESS

PHONE

REFERRED BY

COMMENTS

NAME

ADDRESS

PHONE

REFERRED BY

COMMENTS

NAME

ADDRESS

PHONE

REFERRED BY

COMMENTS

NAME

ADDRESS

PHONE

REFERRED BY

COMMENTS

NAME

ADDRESS

PHONE

REFERRED BY

COMMENTS

NAME

ADDRESS

PHONE

REFERRED BY

COMMENTS

NAME

ADDRESS

PHONE

REFERRED BY

COMMENTS

HAIRDRESSERS & BARBERS

NAME _____

ADDRESS _____

PHONE _____

REFERRED BY _____

COMMENTS _____

_____

NAME _____

ADDRESS _____

PHONE _____

REFERRED BY _____

COMMENTS _____

_____

NAME _____

ADDRESS _____

PHONE _____

REFERRED BY _____

COMMENTS _____

_____

NAME _____

ADDRESS _____

PHONE _____

REFERRED BY _____

COMMENTS _____

_____

NAME

ADDRESS

PHONE

REFERRED BY

COMMENTS

NAME

ADDRESS

PHONE

REFERRED BY

COMMENTS

NAME

ADDRESS

PHONE

REFERRED BY

COMMENTS

NAME

ADDRESS

PHONE

REFERRED BY

COMMENTS

HARDWARE STORES

NAME

ADDRESS

PHONE

REFERRED BY

COMMENTS

NAME

ADDRESS

PHONE

REFERRED BY

COMMENTS

NAME

ADDRESS

PHONE

REFERRED BY

COMMENTS

NAME

ADDRESS

PHONE

REFERRED BY

COMMENTS

NAME

ADDRESS

PHONE

REFERRED BY

COMMENTS

NAME

ADDRESS

PHONE

REFERRED BY

COMMENTS

Fixing on the gutter

NAME

ADDRESS

PHONE

REFERRED BY

COMMENTS

NAME

ADDRESS

PHONE

REFERRED BY

COMMENTS

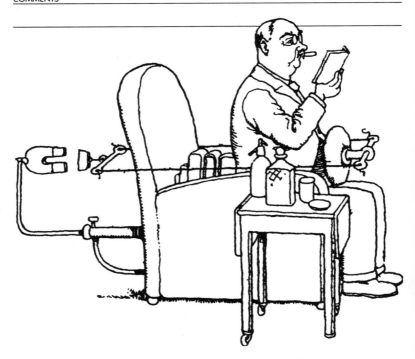

The magnetic figure preserver for the middle-aged

NAME

ADDRESS

PHONE

REFERRED BY

COMMENTS

NAME

ADDRESS

PHONE

REFERRED BY

COMMENTS

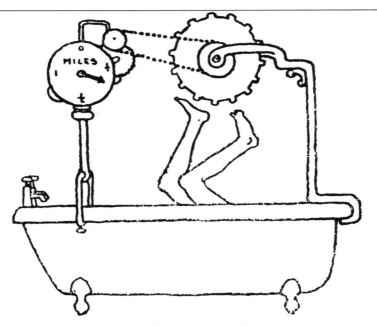

Bathroom exercise for training the legs for running to the station in the morning

NAME

ADDRESS

PHONE

REFERRED BY

COMMENTS

NAME

ADDRESS

PHONE

REFERRED BY

COMMENTS

NAME

ADDRESS

PHONE

REFERRED BY

COMMENTS

NAME

ADDRESS

PHONE

REFERRED BY

COMMENTS

NAME

ADDRESS

PHONE

REFERRED BY

COMMENTS

NAME

ADDRESS

PHONE

REFERRED BY

COMMENTS

An "air frais" bungalow for warm weather

HOSPITALS

NAME

ADDRESS

PHONE

REFERRED BY

COMMENTS

✚

NAME

ADDRESS

PHONE

REFERRED BY

COMMENTS

✚

NAME

ADDRESS

PHONE

REFERRED BY

COMMENTS

✚

NAME

ADDRESS

PHONE

REFERRED BY

COMMENTS

NAME

ADDRESS

PHONE

REFERRED BY

COMMENTS

NAME

ADDRESS

PHONE

REFERRED BY

COMMENTS

NAME

ADDRESS

PHONE

REFERRED BY

COMMENTS

NAME

ADDRESS

PHONE

REFERRED BY

COMMENTS

NAME

ADDRESS

PHONE

REFERRED BY

COMMENTS

NAME

ADDRESS

PHONE

REFERRED BY

COMMENTS

*A new kind of inn sign
for the short-sighted*

NAME

ADDRESS

PHONE

REFERRED BY

COMMENTS

NAME

ADDRESS

PHONE

REFERRED BY

COMMENTS

NAME

ADDRESS

PHONE

REFERRED BY

COMMENTS

NAME

ADDRESS

PHONE

REFERRED BY

COMMENTS

HOUSE SITTERS

NAME

ADDRESS

PHONE

REFERRED BY

COMMENTS

NAME

ADDRESS

PHONE

REFERRED BY

COMMENTS

NAME

ADDRESS

PHONE

REFERRED BY

COMMENTS

NAME

ADDRESS

PHONE

REFERRED BY

COMMENTS

NAME

ADDRESS

PHONE

REFERRED BY

COMMENTS

NAME

ADDRESS

PHONE

REFERRED BY

COMMENTS

NAME

ADDRESS

PHONE

REFERRED BY

COMMENTS

NAME

ADDRESS

PHONE

REFERRED BY

COMMENTS

INTERIOR DECORATORS

NAME

ADDRESS

PHONE

REFERRED BY

COMMENTS

NAME

ADDRESS

PHONE

REFERRED BY

COMMENTS

NAME

ADDRESS

PHONE

REFERRED BY

COMMENTS

NAME

ADDRESS

PHONE

REFERRED BY

COMMENTS

The spare bedroom

INVESTMENT ADVISORS

NAME

ADDRESS

PHONE

REFERRED BY

COMMENTS

NAME

ADDRESS

PHONE

REFERRED BY

COMMENTS

NAME

ADDRESS

PHONE

REFERRED BY

COMMENTS

*Early closing day at
the stock exchange*

NAME _____

ADDRESS _____

PHONE _____

REFERRED BY _____

COMMENTS _____

_____

NAME _____

ADDRESS _____

PHONE _____

REFERRED BY _____

COMMENTS _____

_____

NAME _____

ADDRESS _____

PHONE _____

REFERRED BY _____

COMMENTS _____

_____

NAME _____

ADDRESS _____

PHONE _____

REFERRED BY _____

COMMENTS _____

_____

NAME

ADDRESS

PHONE

REFERRED BY

COMMENTS

NAME

ADDRESS

PHONE

REFERRED BY

COMMENTS

NAME

ADDRESS

PHONE

REFERRED BY

COMMENTS

NAME

ADDRESS

PHONE

REFERRED BY

COMMENTS

NAME

ADDRESS

PHONE

REFERRED BY

COMMENTS

NAME

ADDRESS

PHONE

REFERRED BY

COMMENTS

NAME

ADDRESS

PHONE

REFERRED BY

COMMENTS

NAME

ADDRESS

PHONE

REFERRED BY

COMMENTS

NAME

ADDRESS

PHONE

REFERRED BY

COMMENTS

How to avoid tears when peeling onions

NAME

ADDRESS

PHONE

REFERRED BY

COMMENTS

NAME

ADDRESS

PHONE

REFERRED BY

COMMENTS

NAME

ADDRESS

PHONE

REFERRED BY

COMMENTS

NAME

ADDRESS

PHONE

REFERRED BY

COMMENTS

LANDSCAPERS

NAME _____

ADDRESS _____

PHONE _____

REFERRED BY _____

COMMENTS _____

_____

NAME _____

ADDRESS _____

PHONE _____

REFERRED BY _____

COMMENTS _____

_____

NAME _____

ADDRESS _____

PHONE _____

REFERRED BY _____

COMMENTS _____

_____

Design for a landscape garden

NAME _____

ADDRESS _____

PHONE _____

REFERRED BY _____

COMMENTS _____

_____

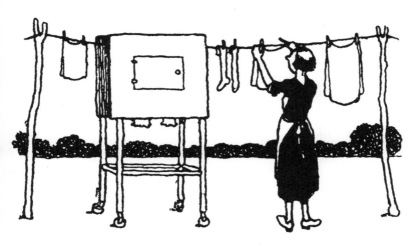

NAME _____

ADDRESS _____

PHONE _____

REFERRED BY _____

COMMENTS _____

_____

*The lingerie modesty screen to avoid embarrassment
on washing day*

NAME

ADDRESS

PHONE

REFERRED BY

COMMENTS

NAME

ADDRESS

PHONE

REFERRED BY

COMMENTS

NAME

ADDRESS

PHONE

REFERRED BY

COMMENTS

NAME

ADDRESS

PHONE

REFERRED BY

COMMENTS

Weeding without treading on the beds

LAWYERS

NAME

ADDRESS

PHONE

REFERRED BY

COMMENTS

NAME

ADDRESS

PHONE

REFERRED BY

COMMENTS

NAME

ADDRESS

PHONE

REFERRED BY

COMMENTS

NAME

ADDRESS

PHONE

REFERRED BY

COMMENTS

NAME

ADDRESS

PHONE

REFERRED BY

COMMENTS

NAME

ADDRESS

PHONE

REFERRED BY

COMMENTS

NAME

ADDRESS

PHONE

REFERRED BY

COMMENTS

LIGHTING:

NAME

ADDRESS

PHONE

REFERRED BY

COMMENTS

NAME

ADDRESS

PHONE

REFERRED BY

COMMENTS

NAME

ADDRESS

PHONE

REFERRED BY

COMMENTS

NAME

ADDRESS

PHONE

REFERRED BY

COMMENTS

NAME

ADDRESS

PHONE

REFERRED BY

COMMENTS

NAME

ADDRESS

PHONE

REFERRED BY

COMMENTS

NAME

ADDRESS

PHONE

REFERRED BY

COMMENTS

NAME

ADDRESS

PHONE

REFERRED BY

COMMENTS

Brighter lamp-posts

NAME

ADDRESS

PHONE

REFERRED BY

COMMENTS

NAME

ADDRESS

PHONE

REFERRED BY

COMMENTS

Newly married couple folding linen

NAME

ADDRESS

PHONE

REFERRED BY

COMMENTS

NAME

ADDRESS

PHONE

REFERRED BY

COMMENTS

NAME

ADDRESS

PHONE

REFERRED BY

COMMENTS

NAME

ADDRESS

PHONE

REFERRED BY

COMMENTS

LIQUOR STORES

NAME _____

ADDRESS _____

PHONE _____

REFERRED BY _____

COMMENTS _____

_____

NAME _____

ADDRESS _____

PHONE _____

REFERRED BY _____

COMMENTS _____

_____

NAME _____

ADDRESS _____

PHONE _____

REFERRED BY _____

COMMENTS _____

_____

NAME _____

ADDRESS _____

PHONE _____

REFERRED BY _____

COMMENTS _____

_____

NAME

ADDRESS

PHONE

REFERRED BY

COMMENTS

NAME

ADDRESS

PHONE

REFERRED BY

COMMENTS

How to train oneself to insert the latchkey in the dark

NAME

ADDRESS

PHONE

REFERRED BY

COMMENTS

NAME

ADDRESS

PHONE

REFERRED BY

COMMENTS

NAME

ADDRESS

PHONE

REFERRED BY

COMMENTS

NAME

ADDRESS

PHONE

REFERRED BY

COMMENTS

NAME

ADDRESS

PHONE

REFERRED BY

COMMENTS

NAME

ADDRESS

PHONE

REFERRED BY

COMMENTS

The new zip-opening letterbox for taking all size letters

NAME

ADDRESS

PHONE

REFERRED BY

COMMENTS

⚓

NAME

ADDRESS

PHONE

REFERRED BY

COMMENTS

*How to pass the time on the river when you
have forgotten how to row*

NAME

ADDRESS

PHONE

REFERRED BY

COMMENTS

NAME

ADDRESS

PHONE

REFERRED BY

COMMENTS

NAME

ADDRESS

PHONE

REFERRED BY

COMMENTS

NAME

ADDRESS

PHONE

REFERRED BY

COMMENTS

MOVERS

NAME _____

ADDRESS _____

PHONE _____

REFERRED BY _____

COMMENTS _____

_____

NAME _____

ADDRESS _____

PHONE _____

REFERRED BY _____

COMMENTS _____

_____

NAME _____

ADDRESS _____

PHONE _____

REFERRED BY _____

COMMENTS _____

_____

NAME _____

ADDRESS _____

PHONE _____

REFERRED BY _____

COMMENTS _____

_____

NAME _____

ADDRESS _____

PHONE _____

REFERRED BY _____

COMMENTS _____

_____

NAME _____

ADDRESS _____

PHONE _____

REFERRED BY _____

COMMENTS _____

_____

*For practicing quietly without
disturbing the neighbors*

NAME

ADDRESS

PHONE

REFERRED BY

COMMENTS

NAME

ADDRESS

PHONE

REFERRED BY

COMMENTS

NAME

ADDRESS

PHONE

REFERRED BY

COMMENTS

NAME

ADDRESS

PHONE

REFERRED BY

COMMENTS

NAME

ADDRESS

PHONE

REFERRED BY

COMMENTS

NAME

ADDRESS

PHONE

REFERRED BY

COMMENTS

NAME

ADDRESS

PHONE

REFERRED BY

COMMENTS

NAME

ADDRESS

PHONE

REFERRED BY

COMMENTS

PAINTERS

NAME _____

ADDRESS _____

PHONE _____

REFERRED BY _____

COMMENTS _____

_____

NAME _____

ADDRESS _____

PHONE _____

REFERRED BY _____

COMMENTS _____

_____

NAME _____

ADDRESS _____

PHONE _____

REFERRED BY _____

COMMENTS _____

_____

NAME _____

ADDRESS _____

PHONE _____

REFERRED BY _____

COMMENTS _____

_____

NAME

ADDRESS

PHONE

REFERRED BY

COMMENTS

NAME

ADDRESS

PHONE

REFERRED BY

COMMENTS

Bridge as usual

PARTY RENTALS

NAME

ADDRESS

PHONE

REFERRED BY

COMMENTS

NAME

ADDRESS

PHONE

REFERRED BY

COMMENTS

NAME

ADDRESS

PHONE

REFERRED BY

COMMENTS

NAME

ADDRESS

PHONE

REFERRED BY

COMMENTS

NAME _____

ADDRESS _____

PHONE _____

REFERRED BY _____

COMMENTS _____

_____

The extending bungalow for week-end parties

Pets' corner, Boldersbury Court, S.W.

NAME _____

ADDRESS _____

PHONE _____

REFERRED BY _____

COMMENTS _____

_____

NAME _____

ADDRESS _____

PHONE _____

REFERRED BY _____

COMMENTS _____

_____

NAME _____

ADDRESS _____

PHONE _____

REFERRED BY _____

COMMENTS _____

_____

NAME _____

ADDRESS _____

PHONE _____

REFERRED BY _____

COMMENTS _____

_____

PHARMACIES

NAME

ADDRESS

PHONE

REFERRED BY

COMMENTS

NAME

ADDRESS

PHONE

REFERRED BY

COMMENTS

NAME

ADDRESS

PHONE

REFERRED BY

COMMENTS

NAME

ADDRESS

PHONE

REFERRED BY

COMMENTS

NAME

ADDRESS

PHONE

REFERRED BY

COMMENTS

NAME

ADDRESS

PHONE

REFERRED BY

COMMENTS

NAME

ADDRESS

PHONE

REFERRED BY

COMMENTS

NAME

ADDRESS

PHONE

REFERRED BY

COMMENTS

PIANO TUNERS

NAME

ADDRESS

PHONE

REFERRED BY

COMMENTS

NAME

ADDRESS

PHONE

REFERRED BY

COMMENTS

NAME

ADDRESS

PHONE

REFERRED BY

COMMENTS

Music cum comfort

NAME

ADDRESS

PHONE

REFERRED BY

COMMENTS

NAME

ADDRESS

PHONE

REFERRED BY

COMMENTS

L'art mutuel

PLANT NURSERIES

NAME _____

ADDRESS _____

PHONE _____

REFERRED BY _____

COMMENTS _____

_____

NAME _____

ADDRESS _____

PHONE _____

REFERRED BY _____

COMMENTS _____

_____

NAME _____

ADDRESS _____

PHONE _____

REFERRED BY _____

COMMENTS _____

_____

NAME _____

ADDRESS _____

PHONE _____

REFERRED BY _____

COMMENTS _____

_____

*Window-box greenhouse
for those without a garden*

NAME

ADDRESS

PHONE

REFERRED BY

COMMENTS

*Waiting for the plumber to deal with
the leak in the linen cupboard*

NAME

ADDRESS

PHONE

REFERRED BY

COMMENTS

NAME

ADDRESS

PHONE

REFERRED BY

COMMENTS

NAME

ADDRESS

PHONE

REFERRED BY

COMMENTS

The washer-trouble overcome

The last collection

NAME _____

ADDRESS _____

PHONE _____

REFERRED BY _____

COMMENTS _____

_____

NAME _____

ADDRESS _____

PHONE _____

REFERRED BY _____

COMMENTS _____

_____

NAME _____

ADDRESS _____

PHONE _____

REFERRED BY _____

COMMENTS _____

_____

NAME _____

ADDRESS _____

PHONE _____

REFERRED BY _____

COMMENTS _____

_____

RAILROADS

NAME

ADDRESS

PHONE

REFERRED BY

COMMENTS

#####

NAME

ADDRESS

PHONE

REFERRED BY

COMMENTS

#####

NAME

ADDRESS

PHONE

REFERRED BY

COMMENTS

#####

NAME

ADDRESS

PHONE

REFERRED BY

COMMENTS

NAME _____

ADDRESS _____

PHONE _____

REFERRED BY _____

COMMENTS _____

_____

NAME _____

ADDRESS _____

PHONE _____

REFERRED BY _____

COMMENTS _____

_____

Proving that there is room to swing a cat

REAL-ESTATE AGENCIES

NAME

ADDRESS

PHONE

REFERRED BY

COMMENTS

NAME

ADDRESS

PHONE

REFERRED BY

COMMENTS

NAME

ADDRESS

PHONE

REFERRED BY

COMMENTS

NAME

ADDRESS

PHONE

REFERRED BY

COMMENTS

NAME

ADDRESS

PHONE

REFERRED BY

COMMENTS

NAME

ADDRESS

PHONE

REFERRED BY

COMMENTS

NAME

ADDRESS

PHONE

REFERRED BY

COMMENTS

NAME

ADDRESS

PHONE

REFERRED BY

COMMENTS

RESTAURANTS

NAME

ADDRESS

PHONE

REFERRED BY

COMMENTS

NAME

ADDRESS

PHONE

REFERRED BY

COMMENTS

NAME

ADDRESS

PHONE

REFERRED BY

COMMENTS

NAME

ADDRESS

PHONE

REFERRED BY

COMMENTS

NAME

ADDRESS

PHONE

REFERRED BY

COMMENTS

NAME

ADDRESS

PHONE

REFERRED BY

COMMENTS

The cold egg

NAME

ADDRESS

PHONE

REFERRED BY

COMMENTS

For the prevention of breakfast-time acerbities

NAME _____

ADDRESS _____

PHONE _____

REFERRED BY _____

COMMENTS _____

_____

NAME _____

ADDRESS _____

PHONE _____

REFERRED BY _____

COMMENTS _____

_____

NAME _____

ADDRESS _____

PHONE _____

REFERRED BY _____

COMMENTS _____

_____

NAME _____

ADDRESS _____

PHONE _____

REFERRED BY _____

COMMENTS _____

_____

RESTAURANTS

NAME

ADDRESS

PHONE

REFERRED BY

COMMENTS

NAME

ADDRESS

PHONE

REFERRED BY

COMMENTS

NAME

ADDRESS

PHONE

REFERRED BY

COMMENTS

NAME

ADDRESS

PHONE

REFERRED BY

COMMENTS

NAME

ADDRESS

PHONE

REFERRED BY

COMMENTS

NAME

ADDRESS

PHONE

REFERRED BY

COMMENTS

Crazy pavement for the roof garden

SCHOOLS

NAME

ADDRESS

PHONE

REFERRED BY

COMMENTS

NAME

ADDRESS

PHONE

REFERRED BY

COMMENTS

NAME

ADDRESS

PHONE

REFERRED BY

COMMENTS

NAME

ADDRESS

PHONE

REFERRED BY

COMMENTS

NAME _____

ADDRESS _____

PHONE _____

REFERRED BY _____

COMMENTS _____

_____

NAME _____

ADDRESS _____

PHONE _____

REFERRED BY _____

COMMENTS _____

_____

Teaching geography: an opportunity not to be missed

NAME _____

ADDRESS _____

PHONE _____

REFERRED BY _____

COMMENTS _____

_____

NAME _____

ADDRESS _____

PHONE _____

REFERRED BY _____

COMMENTS _____

_____

An amusing method of explaining the planetary system to the young

NAME

ADDRESS

PHONE

REFERRED BY

COMMENTS

NAME

ADDRESS

PHONE

REFERRED BY

COMMENTS

Remorse

NAME

ADDRESS

PHONE

REFERRED BY

COMMENTS

NAME

ADDRESS

PHONE

REFERRED BY

COMMENTS

For wiping the shoes on muddy days

NAME

ADDRESS

PHONE

REFERRED BY

COMMENTS

NAME

ADDRESS

PHONE

REFERRED BY

COMMENTS

NAME

ADDRESS

PHONE

REFERRED BY

COMMENTS

NAME

ADDRESS

PHONE

REFERRED BY

COMMENTS

SOUND PROOFING

NAME

ADDRESS

PHONE

REFERRED BY

COMMENTS

•)))▌

NAME

ADDRESS

PHONE

REFERRED BY

COMMENTS

•)))▌

NAME

ADDRESS

PHONE

REFERRED BY

COMMENTS

•)))▌

NAME

ADDRESS

PHONE

REFERRED BY

COMMENTS

The sneeze

SPORTING GOODS

NAME

ADDRESS

PHONE

REFERRED BY

COMMENTS

NAME

ADDRESS

PHONE

REFERRED BY

COMMENTS

NAME

ADDRESS

PHONE

REFERRED BY

COMMENTS

NAME

ADDRESS

PHONE

REFERRED BY

COMMENTS

NAME _____

ADDRESS _____

PHONE _____

REFERRED BY _____

COMMENTS _____

_____

NAME _____

ADDRESS _____

PHONE _____

REFERRED BY _____

COMMENTS _____

_____

Musical croquet

NAME

ADDRESS

PHONE

REFERRED BY

COMMENTS

The bungalow kitchenette

NAME

ADDRESS

PHONE

REFERRED BY

COMMENTS

NAME

ADDRESS

PHONE

REFERRED BY

COMMENTS

NAME

ADDRESS

PHONE

REFERRED BY

COMMENTS

NAME

ADDRESS

PHONE

REFERRED BY

COMMENTS

NAME

ADDRESS

PHONE

REFERRED BY

COMMENTS

NAME

ADDRESS

PHONE

REFERRED BY

COMMENTS

*The new diving boat
(for those lacking sufficient courage to take the plunge)*

NAME

ADDRESS

PHONE

REFERRED BY

COMMENTS

NAME

ADDRESS

PHONE

REFERRED BY

COMMENTS

NAME

ADDRESS

PHONE

REFERRED BY

COMMENTS

NAME

ADDRESS

PHONE

REFERRED BY

COMMENTS

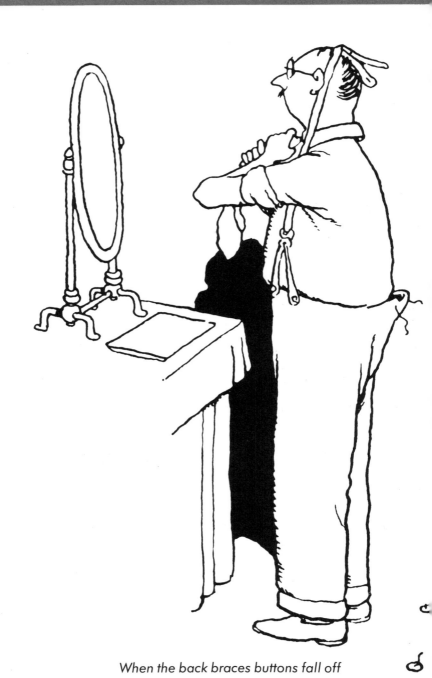

When the back braces buttons fall off

NAME

ADDRESS

PHONE

REFERRED BY

COMMENTS

NAME

ADDRESS

PHONE

REFERRED BY

COMMENTS

NAME

ADDRESS

PHONE

REFERRED BY

COMMENTS

NAME

ADDRESS

PHONE

REFERRED BY

COMMENTS

TAKE-OUT RESTAURANTS

NAME _____

ADDRESS _____

PHONE _____

REFERRED BY _____

COMMENTS _____

_____

NAME _____

ADDRESS _____

PHONE _____

REFERRED BY _____

COMMENTS _____

_____

See that your secretary gets a little healthy exercise in the lunch hour

NAME

ADDRESS

PHONE

REFERRED BY

COMMENTS

NAME

ADDRESS

PHONE

REFERRED BY

COMMENTS

NAME

ADDRESS

PHONE

REFERRED BY

COMMENTS

NAME

ADDRESS

PHONE

REFERRED BY

COMMENTS

TAKE-OUT RESTAURANTS

NAME

ADDRESS

PHONE

REFERRED BY

COMMENTS

NAME

ADDRESS

PHONE

REFERRED BY

COMMENTS

NAME

ADDRESS

PHONE

REFERRED BY

COMMENTS

NAME

ADDRESS

PHONE

REFERRED BY

COMMENTS

NAME

ADDRESS

PHONE

REFERRED BY

COMMENTS

NAME

ADDRESS

PHONE

REFERRED BY

COMMENTS

NAME

ADDRESS

PHONE

REFERRED BY

COMMENTS

The new way of hailing taxis

NAME

ADDRESS

PHONE

REFERRED BY

COMMENTS

NAME

ADDRESS

PHONE

REFERRED BY

COMMENTS

NAME

ADDRESS

PHONE

REFERRED BY

COMMENTS

NAME

ADDRESS

PHONE

REFERRED BY

COMMENTS

NAME

ADDRESS

PHONE

REFERRED BY

COMMENTS

NAME

ADDRESS

PHONE

REFERRED BY

COMMENTS

NAME

ADDRESS

PHONE

REFERRED BY

COMMENTS

NAME

ADDRESS

PHONE

REFERRED BY

COMMENTS

TELEVISION & RADIO:
SUPPLIERS, SERVICES, REPAIR

NAME

ADDRESS

PHONE

REFERRED BY

COMMENTS

NAME

ADDRESS

PHONE

REFERRED BY

COMMENTS

NAME

ADDRESS

PHONE

REFERRED BY

COMMENTS

NAME

ADDRESS

PHONE

REFERRED BY

COMMENTS

NAME _____

ADDRESS _____

PHONE _____

REFERRED BY _____

COMMENTS _____

_____

The mind of a woman works in mysterious ways

TENNIS COURTS

NAME

ADDRESS

PHONE

REFERRED BY

COMMENTS

NAME

ADDRESS

PHONE

REFERRED BY

COMMENTS

NAME

ADDRESS

PHONE

REFERRED BY

COMMENTS

NAME

ADDRESS

PHONE

REFERRED BY

COMMENTS

NAME _____

ADDRESS _____

PHONE _____

REFERRED BY _____

COMMENTS _____

_____

NAME _____

ADDRESS _____

PHONE _____

REFERRED BY _____

COMMENTS _____

_____

NAME _____

ADDRESS _____

PHONE _____

REFERRED BY _____

COMMENTS _____

_____

NAME _____

ADDRESS _____

PHONE _____

REFERRED BY _____

COMMENTS _____

_____

NAME

ADDRESS

PHONE

REFERRED BY

COMMENTS

NAME

ADDRESS

PHONE

REFERRED BY

COMMENTS

NAME

ADDRESS

PHONE

REFERRED BY

COMMENTS

NAME

ADDRESS

PHONE

REFERRED BY

COMMENTS

NAME

ADDRESS

PHONE

REFERRED BY

COMMENTS

NAME

ADDRESS

PHONE

REFERRED BY

COMMENTS

Evading the customs

NAME

ADDRESS

PHONE

REFERRED BY

COMMENTS

NAME

ADDRESS

PHONE

REFERRED BY

COMMENTS

A well-trained tree

NAME

ADDRESS

PHONE

REFERRED BY

COMMENTS

NAME

ADDRESS

PHONE

REFERRED BY

COMMENTS

NAME

ADDRESS

PHONE

REFERRED BY

COMMENTS

NAME

ADDRESS

PHONE

REFERRED BY

COMMENTS

NAME _____

ADDRESS _____

PHONE _____

REFERRED BY _____

COMMENTS _____

_____

NAME _____

ADDRESS _____

PHONE _____

REFERRED BY _____

COMMENTS _____

The expando fireside settee

NAME _____

ADDRESS _____

PHONE _____

REFERRED BY _____

COMMENTS _____

_____

NAME _____

ADDRESS _____

PHONE _____

REFERRED BY _____

COMMENTS _____

_____

NAME _____

ADDRESS _____

PHONE _____

REFERRED BY _____

COMMENTS _____

_____

NAME _____

ADDRESS _____

PHONE _____

REFERRED BY _____

COMMENTS _____

_____

NAME

ADDRESS

PHONE

REFERRED BY

COMMENTS

Listening to an ailing goldfish

NAME _____

ADDRESS _____

PHONE _____

REFERRED BY _____

COMMENTS _____

_____

NAME _____

ADDRESS _____

PHONE _____

REFERRED BY _____

COMMENTS _____

_____

NAME _____

ADDRESS _____

PHONE _____

REFERRED BY _____

COMMENTS _____

_____

NAME _____

ADDRESS _____

PHONE _____

REFERRED BY _____

COMMENTS _____

_____

NAME

ADDRESS

PHONE

REFERRED BY

COMMENTS

NAME

ADDRESS

PHONE

REFERRED BY

COMMENTS

NAME

ADDRESS

PHONE

REFERRED BY

COMMENTS

NAME

ADDRESS

PHONE

REFERRED BY

COMMENTS

NAME

ADDRESS

PHONE

REFERRED BY

COMMENTS

NAME

ADDRESS

PHONE

REFERRED BY

COMMENTS

NAME

ADDRESS

PHONE

REFERRED BY

COMMENTS

NAME

ADDRESS

PHONE

REFERRED BY

COMMENTS

NAME

ADDRESS

PHONE

REFERRED BY

COMMENTS

NAME

ADDRESS

PHONE

REFERRED BY

COMMENTS

NAME

ADDRESS

PHONE

REFERRED BY

COMMENTS

NAME

ADDRESS

PHONE

REFERRED BY

COMMENTS

As if she were a piece of genuine Sèvres

NAME

ADDRESS

PHONE

REFERRED BY

COMMENTS

NAME

ADDRESS

PHONE

REFERRED BY

COMMENTS

NAME

ADDRESS

PHONE

REFERRED BY

COMMENTS

NAME

ADDRESS

PHONE

REFERRED BY

COMMENTS

NAME _____

ADDRESS _____

PHONE _____

REFERRED BY _____

COMMENTS _____

_____

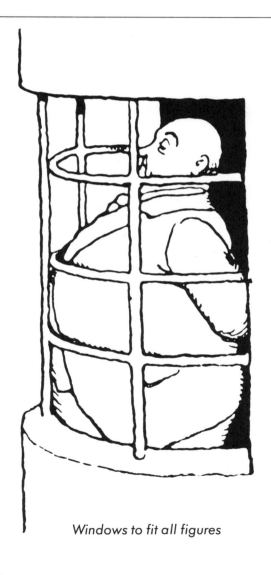

Windows to fit all figures

NAME

ADDRESS

PHONE

REFERRED BY

COMMENTS

NAME

ADDRESS

PHONE

REFERRED BY

COMMENTS

Restoration

NAME

ADDRESS

PHONE

REFERRED BY

COMMENTS

NAME

ADDRESS

PHONE

REFERRED BY

COMMENTS

NAME

ADDRESS

PHONE

REFERRED BY

COMMENTS

NAME

ADDRESS

PHONE

REFERRED BY

COMMENTS

NAME _____

ADDRESS _____

PHONE _____

REFERRED BY _____

COMMENTS _____

_____

✆

NAME _____

ADDRESS _____

PHONE _____

REFERRED BY _____

COMMENTS _____

_____

✆

NAME _____

ADDRESS _____

PHONE _____

REFERRED BY _____

COMMENTS _____

_____

✆

NAME _____

ADDRESS _____

PHONE _____

REFERRED BY _____

COMMENTS _____

_____

NAME _____

ADDRESS _____

PHONE _____

REFERRED BY _____

COMMENTS _____

_____

NAME _____

ADDRESS _____

PHONE _____

REFERRED BY _____

COMMENTS _____

_____

NAME _____

ADDRESS _____

PHONE _____

REFERRED BY _____

COMMENTS _____

_____

NAME _____

ADDRESS _____

PHONE _____

REFERRED BY _____

COMMENTS _____

_____

NAME _____

ADDRESS _____

PHONE _____

REFERRED BY _____

COMMENTS _____

_____

☎

NAME _____

ADDRESS _____

PHONE _____

REFERRED BY _____

COMMENTS _____

_____

☎

NAME _____

ADDRESS _____

PHONE _____

REFERRED BY _____

COMMENTS _____

_____

☎

NAME _____

ADDRESS _____

PHONE _____

REFERRED BY _____

COMMENTS _____

_____

NAME _____

ADDRESS _____

PHONE _____

REFERRED BY _____

COMMENTS _____

_____

NAME _____

ADDRESS _____

PHONE _____

REFERRED BY _____

COMMENTS _____

_____

Combined umbrella and weed-killer

Washing day

NAME

ADDRESS

PHONE

REFERRED BY

COMMENTS

NAME

ADDRESS

PHONE

REFERRED BY

COMMENTS

NAME

ADDRESS

PHONE

REFERRED BY

COMMENTS

NAME

ADDRESS

PHONE

REFERRED BY

COMMENTS

NAME

ADDRESS

PHONE

REFERRED BY

COMMENTS

NAME

ADDRESS

PHONE

REFERRED BY

COMMENTS

NAME

ADDRESS

PHONE

REFERRED BY

COMMENTS

NAME

ADDRESS

PHONE

REFERRED BY

COMMENTS

NAME

ADDRESS

PHONE

REFERRED BY

COMMENTS

NAME

ADDRESS

PHONE

REFERRED BY

COMMENTS

*How to brush the back of your coat
without troubling your wife*

NAME

ADDRESS

PHONE

REFERRED BY

COMMENTS

NAME

ADDRESS

PHONE

REFERRED BY

COMMENTS

How to go to bed without disturbing the household after a late night

NAME

ADDRESS

PHONE

REFERRED BY

COMMENTS

NAME

ADDRESS

PHONE

REFERRED BY

COMMENTS

NAME

ADDRESS

PHONE

REFERRED BY

COMMENTS

NAME

ADDRESS

PHONE

REFERRED BY

COMMENTS

The end